PHARMACOLOGY

*A Comprehensive Reference
Guide for Medical, Nursing, and
Paramedic Students*

Workbook

M. Mastenbjörk MD
S. Meloni MD

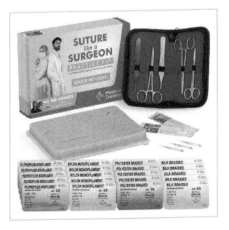
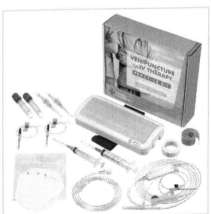

Contents

FREE GIFT

GET ONE OF THESE EBOOKS FOR FREE:

Medical Reference Pamphlet
ACLS ebook
Pulmonology ebook
Neurology ebook
Mini Medical Dictionary

Scan the following QR code:

You will be redirected to our website.
Follow the instructions to claim your free gift.

INTRODUCTION

An incursion into any branch of medicine cannot be complete without a fundamental understanding of the principles of pharmacology. What is the chemical nature of drugs? How do they act in the body? What are their adverse effects and contraindications? These are just some of the important questions that pharmacology answers.

For a succinct yet comprehensive guide to pharmacology, please check our Pharmacology textbook **medicalcreations.net/pharmacology**. It contains all the essential information about drug classes, their mechanisms of action, clinical applications and contraindications.

This Pharmacology workbook aims to complement the textbook. Once you're through with the textbook, you can test your knowledge using the exercises given in this workbook. On the other hand, if you're already feeling pretty confident about your Pharma know-how, you can jump directly to the exercises in this workbook and see how you score.

Good luck!

UNIT I

The Basics

CHAPTER 1

Routes of drug administration

EXERCISE 1 - FILL IN THE BLANKS

1. The ideal route of administration for a drug depends on its _____ and desired effects.

2. The two main routes of drug administration are local/topical and _____.

3. The nasal route is preferred when the drug action is specifically desired for the _____ epithelium.

4. The _____ route is useful for drugs that cannot penetrate the blood-brain barrier.

5. A topical drug is one that is directly applied to the surface of the _____.

6. The _____ route is the most commonly used route of drug administration.

7. The area under the tongue has a rich _____ which can facilitate quick absorption of drugs.

8. In a drug given via the rectal route, the portion of the drug that is absorbed from the external hemorrhoidal veins bypasses _____.

EXERCISE 2 - MCQs

9. Which of the following properties of a drug influence its route of administration?

    a. Lipid solubility
    b. Ionization
    c. Particle size
    d. All of the above

10. A bronchodilator is being considered for an 8-year-old boy with asthma. The doctor wants to maximize the local effect of the drug and minimize its systemic actions. Which one of the following routes of administration would be most appropriate?

    a. topical
    b. inhalational
    c. intrathecal
    d. intranasal

11. A 58-year-old man is being treated for acute meningitis. The doctor has selected an antibiotic based on the culture and sensitivity results of a CSF sample. Which one of the following routes of administration will ensure effective and rapid delivery of the antibiotic?

    a. topical
    b. inhalational
    c. intrathecal
    d. intranasal

12. Which one of the following routes of drug administration would involve first-pass metabolism?

    a. inhalational
    b. transdermal
    c. oral
    d. sublingual

13. Which of the following routes of drug administration can be categorized as parenteral?

    a. Subcutaneous
    b. Intravenous
    c. Intramuscular
    d. All of the above

14. Which one of the following parenteral routes of drug administration is characterized by having the slowest release of the drug into the circulation?

    a. Subcutaneous   c. Intramuscular
    b. Intravenous   d. Intrathecal

15. Which one of the following parenteral routes of drug administration can be utilized to precisely control plasma drug concentrations through a titrated infusion?

    a. Subcutaneous   c. Intramuscular
    b. Intravenous   d. Intrathecal

16. Which one of the following statements is true for the intramuscular route?

    a. The drug is injected into adipose tissue.
    b. Drugs in aqueous solutions are absorbed quickly.
    c. Anticoagulants should be administered through this route.
    d. The route involves first-pass metabolism.

CHAPTER 2:

Drug-body interactions: pharmacokinetics and pharmacodynamics

EXERCISE 1 - FILL IN THE BLANKS

1. _____ describes what the body does to the drug.

2. _____ describes what the drug does to the body.

3. The extent to which a drug is absorbed determines its _____.

4. Lipid soluble drugs pass easily through the phospholipid bilayer of the _____.

5. A drug that has a low pKa (or is acidic) tends to have a higher amount of unionized form when the surrounding pH is _____.

6. The epithelial lining of the small intestine has _____ which greatly increase the surface area for absorption.

7. The brain has tight endothelial cell-to-cell contact, referred to as the _____.

EXERCISE 2 - MCQs

8. Which one of the following belongs to the pharmacodynamics of a drug?

    a. absorption
    b. receptor-binding

    c. metabolism
    d. elimination

9. Which one of the following routes of drug administration allows 100% bioavailability of the drug?

    a. Oral
    b. Intravenous

    c. Intramuscular
    d. Topical

10. Which one of the following modes of drug transport is not energy-dependent?

    a. Facilitated diffusion
    b. Active transport
    c. Endocytosis
    d. All of the above

11. Drugs with a large molecular size are often absorbed through:

    a. Passive diffusion
    b. Facilitated diffusion

    c. Active transport
    d. Endocytosis

12. The main drug-binding protein in blood is:

    a. Albumin
    b. Globulin

    c. Fibrinogen
    d. Thrombin

EXERCISE 3 - LABEL THE PICTURE

Label the four types of receptors in the image below.

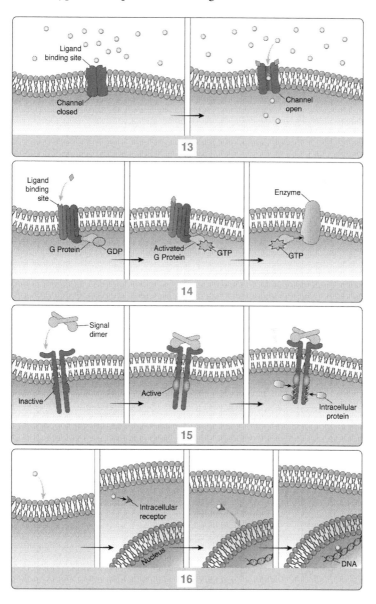

13. _____   15. _____

14. _____   16. _____

UNIT II

Central Nervous System

CHAPTER 1:

General anesthetics

EXERCISE 1 - FILL IN THE BLANKS

1. The term anesthesia refers to loss of sensation. 'General' anesthesia is the term used when loss of sensation is accompanied by loss of _____.

2. Preanesthetic medication is the administration of certain drugs _____ a procedure to smoothen the process of anesthesia and decrease its side effects.

3. _____ drugs such as ondansetron, metoclopramide and domperidone, help decrease the incidence of postoperative nausea and vomiting, which is a side effect of several anesthetic agents.

4. While induction of general anesthesia is done using intravenous drugs, it is maintained at the desired depth using _____ drugs.

5. The recovery phase of general anesthesia is essentially the reverse of _____.

6. During recovery from general anesthesia, reversal agents may be required for removing neuromuscular blockage caused by _____.

7. Highly potent inhalational anesthetics have _____ minimum alveolar concentration (MAC) values.

8. Alveolar wash-in is the period in which the normal gases in the lungs are pushed out and replaced with the _____.

EXERCISE 2 - MCQs

9. Which one of the following is NOT a desired effect of general anesthesia?

    a. Suppressed or complete loss of consciousness
    b. Amnesia and reduction in anxiety levels
    c. Suppression of pain and reflexes
    d. Skeletal muscle rigidity

10. Glycopyrrolate, an anticholinergic drug, is a commonly used preanesthetic medication. It helps to prevent which of the following conditions?

    a. Bradycardia
    b. Hypotension
    c. Laryngospasm
    d. All of the above

11. Which one of the following represents the third stage of anesthesia depth?

    a. Excitement and delirium
    b. Surgical anesthesia
    c. Analgesia
    d. Medullary paralysis

12. Which one of the following stages representing the depth of anesthesia is characterized by depression of the respiratory and vasomotor centers of the brain?

    a. Excitement and delirium
    b. Surgical anesthesia
    c. Analgesia
    d. Medullary paralysis

13. Which one of the following stages representing the depth of anesthesia is characterized by the progressive loss of the corneal, laryngeal and light reflexes?

    a. Excitement and delirium
    b. Surgical anesthesia
    c. Analgesia
    d. Medullary paralysis

14. Which of the following factors play a role in the uptake of the anesthetic agent by tissues?

    a. Solubility
    b. Cardiac output
    c. Tissue vascularity
    d. All of the above

15. Halothane is being used to maintain anesthesia in a patient undergoing a surgical procedure. The patient's temperature begins to rise suddenly and malignant hyperthermia is suspected. After immediately stopping the supply of halothane to the patient, which drug should be given as an antidote?

    a. Isoflurane   c. Dantrolene sodium
    b. Acetaminophen   d. Naloxone

16. Which one of the following inhaled anesthetic agents has to be delivered through a special heated vaporizer because of its low volatility?

    a. Isoflurane   c. Sevoflurane
    b. Desflurane   d. Nitrous oxide

17. Which one of the following inhaled anesthetic agents has very rapid induction and recovery and is therefore very suited for outpatient procedures?

    a. Isoflurane   c. Sevoflurane
    b. Desflurane   d. Nitrous oxide

CHAPTER 2:

Sedative-hypnotic drugs

EXERCISE 1 - FILL IN THE BLANKS

1. Sedatives, also known as anxiolytics, calm the patient, while _____ induce normal, arousable sleep.

2. Benzodiazepines act at the _____ receptor.

3. Benzodiazepines can cross the placental barrier and depress the _____ CNS.

4. If high doses of benzodiazepines are used for long periods of time, physical and _____ dependence can develop.

5. Benzodiazepines should not be routinely prescribed to alleviate the normal _____ of day-to-day living.

EXERCISE 2 - MCQs

6. Which one of the following is an effect of an activated GABA receptor?

    a. Efflux of chloride from the neuron
    b. Triggering an action potential
    c. Hyperpolarizing the neuron
    d. Blocking benzodiazepine attachment

7. Which one of the following clinical effects is NOT associated with benzodiazepines?

    a. Reduction of anxiety
    b. Retrograde amnesia
    c. Anticonvulsant activity
    d. Muscle relaxation

8. Which one of the following is a short-acting benzodiazepine?

    a. Diazepam   c. Temazepam
    b. Alprazolam   d. Triazolam

9. Which one of the following is a long-acting benzodiazepine?

    a. Diazepam   c. Temazepam
    b. Alprazolam   d. Triazolam

10. Which one of the following benzodiazepines is the drug of choice for termination of status epilepticus?

    a. Diazepam   c. Temazepam
    b. Alprazolam   d. Triazolam

CHAPTER 3:

Opioid analgesics

EXERCISE 1 - FILL IN THE BLANKS

1. The body produces endogenous opioids, such as _____ and enkephalins.

2. Opioids bind to three receptor sites on the neuronal surface – the μ, κ and _____ receptors.

3. Some opioids, like _____, also alter the brain's perception of pain, bringing further pain relief.

4. _____ is twice as potent as morphine when given orally.

5. Morphine is usually administered parenterally because it undergoes high _____.

EXERCISE 2 - MCQs

6. Which one of the following is an effect of activated opioid receptors?

    a. Activation of adenylyl cyclase
    b. Efflux of calcium ions from the neuron
    c. Influx of potassium ions into the neuron
    d. Attenuation of pain impulse

7. Which one of the following is the major cause of death after an opioid overdose?

    a. Myocardial infarction
    b. Respiratory depression
    c. Stroke
    d. Liver failure

8. Which one of the following clinical conditions is associated with morphine use?

    a. Pupillary mydriasis
    b. Dysphoria
    c. Constipation
    d. Coughing

CHAPTER 4:

Antidepressants and anti-anxiety drugs

EXERCISE 1 - FILL IN THE BLANKS

1. In bipolar disorders, bouts of depression alternate with bouts of
   _____.

2. The 'amine theory' of depression states that depression is caused by a functional deficiency of _____.

3. Most antidepressants work by inhibiting the _____ of the neurotransmitter.

4. SNRIs act by preventing the reuptake of both serotonin and
   _____.

5. SNRIs are indicated to treat depression in cases where SSRIs have proven ineffective or for depression-associated _____.

6. _____, an SNRI, has maximum liver metabolism and should be avoided in patients with liver disease.

EXERCISE 2 - MCQs

7. Which one of the following classes of antidepressants is usually the first-line drugs used in the treatment of depression?

    a. SSRIs
    b. SNRIs
    c. MAOIs
    d. TCAs

8. Which one of the following SSRIs can cause cardiac arrhythmias in case of an overdose?

    a. Sertraline
    b. Fluoxetine
    c. Paroxetine
    d. Citalopram

9. A serotonin syndrome manifested by hyperthermia, muscle rigidity, myoclonus, and alterations in vital signs and mental status can occur if an SSRI is taken with a:

    a. SNRI
    b. MAOI
    c. TCA
    d. Atypical antidepressant

10. All SNRIs are taken:

    a. Subcutaneously
    b. Topically
    c. Orally
    d. Intravenously

11. Which one of the following is INCORRECT regarding the pharmacokinetics of TCAs?

    a. Route of administration is oral.
    b. Bioavailability is unpredictable due to high first-pass metabolism.
    c. TCAs are hydrophilic and cannot penetrate the CNS.
    d. Metabolism occurs in the liver through the cytochrome P450 system as well as conjugation.

12. Which one of the following TCAs has been used to control bed-wetting in children older than six years of age?

    a. Amitriptyline
    b. Imipramine
    c. Doxepin
    d. Maprotiline

CHAPTER 5:

Antipsychotic drugs

EXERCISE 1 - FILL IN THE BLANKS

1. Antipsychotics are a specific class of drugs that are primarily used in the treatment of _____.

2. First generation antipsychotic drugs act by competitively blocking dopamine D2 receptors of all the neuronal pathways except for the _____ area.

3. In normal individuals, antipsychotic drugs can produce '_____ anesthesia.'

EXERCISE 2 - MCQs

4. According to the 'dopamine hypothesis,' psychotic disorders such as schizophrenia occur due to the dysregulation of dopamine in the neurological pathways of the brain. Specifically, there is hyperactivity of dopamine in which one of the following areas of the brain?

   a. mesolimbic area
   b. mesocortical area
   c. tuberoinfundibular area
   d. nigrostriatal area

5. Which one of the following antipsychotic agents is an example of a low potency first generation antipsychotic drug?

   a. Haloperidol
   b. Fluphenazine
   c. Prochlorperazine
   d. Risperidone

6. The extrapyramidal effects of antipsychotic agents occur due to the blockade of which type of receptors in the nigrostriatal pathway?

   a. 5-HT2A
   b. D2
   c. Cholinergic
   d. GABA

CHAPTER 6:

Drugs used in Parkinsonism

EXERCISE 1 - FILL IN THE BLANKS

1. Parkinson's disease is a neurodegenerative disease that affects areas of the brain that control _____.

2. Parkinson's disease is characterized by a deficiency of dopamine in the neostriatum and an increase in _____.

3. Peripherally converted dopamine from L-dopa acts on β-adrenergic receptors leading to tachycardia and _____.

EXERCISE 2 - MCQs

4. L-dopa is used instead of dopamine itself to treat Parkinson's disease because dopamine:

   a. Is not available in tablet form.
   b. Cannot cross the blood-brain barrier.
   c. Cannot be metabolized in the body.
   d. Is too fast-acting.

5. Using L-dopa with which one of the following groups of drugs can result in a hypertensive crisis?

   a. Antiemetics
   b. Antibiotics
   c. MAOIs
   d. TCAs

6. L-dopa is primarily indicated at which stage of Parkinson's disease?

   a. Early
   b. Middle
   c. Late
   d. All of the above

CHAPTER 7:

Anti-epileptic drugs

EXERCISE 1 - FILL IN THE BLANKS

1. _____ seizures are characterized by a self-limiting loss of consciousness.

2. _____ is a life-threatening condition characterized by a series of seizures without recovery of consciousness in between.

3. _____ seizures are a reverse of tonic seizures and are characterized by a sudden loss of muscle tone.

EXERCISE 2 - MCQs

4. Which one of the following drugs used to treat seizures is classified as an aliphatic carboxylic acid?

   a. Phenytoin   c. Sodium valproate
   b. Carbamazepine   d. Pregabalin

5. Hydantoin drugs act by binding and blocking voltage-gated:

   a. Calcium channels   c. Potassium channels
   b. Sodium channels   d. Chloride channels

6. Which one of the following is NOT an adverse effect of hydantoin drugs?

   a. Gingival hypertrophy c. Microcytic anemia
   b. Osteomalacia   d. Fetal cleft lip

25

UNIT III

Autonomic Nervous System

CHAPTER 1:

Cholinergic and anticholinergic drugs

EXERCISE 1 - SYMPATHETIC OR PARASYMPATHETIC

Each of the following statements reflects a property or effect of the sympathetic (S) or parasympathetic (P) nervous system. Accordingly, mark each statement with S or P.

	Property or Effect	S or P
1.	Transmitted through cranial nerves II, VII, IX and X	
2.	Short postsynaptic axons	
3.	Pupillary constriction	
4.	Bronchodilation	
5.	Bladder contraction	

EXERCISE 2 - FILL IN THE BLANKS

6. The NN receptors are found in the adrenal medulla and _____.

7. Receptors specific to the sympathetic nervous system are called _____ receptors and are classified into two broad types: α receptors and β receptors.

8. Acetylcholine acts as a neurotransmitter in two kinds of cholinergic neurons – nicotinic and _____.

9. Free choline from plasma is taken into the neuron where it combines with Coenzyme A to form acetylcholine. The enzyme that catalyzes this reaction is _____.

10. In the GIT, acetylcholine is responsible for increasing smooth muscle tone and peristalsis as well as evacuation of bowel. These effects are mediated through the _____ receptor subtype.

11. _____ is an anticholinesterase agent that has a greater effect on the skeletal muscles, therefore it is used for the management of myasthenia gravis.

12. Edrophonium is a short-acting anticholinesterase agent that is primarily used for the diagnosis of _____.

13. Donepezil, galantamine and rivastigmine are cholinesterase inhibitors that are specifically used in the management of _____.

EXERCISE 3 - MCQs

14. Nicotinic receptors are activated by which neurotransmitter?

    a. Epinephrine   c. Acetylcholine
    b. Glycine   d. Noradrenaline

15. Which one of the following subtypes of muscarinic receptors are found in the heart?

    a. M1   c. M3
    b. M2   d. M5

16. Which one of the following drugs is an example of a directly acting cholinergic drug?

    a. Neostigmine   c. Pilocarpine
    b. Echothiophate   d. Pralidoxime

17. Which one of the following drugs is an example of an indirectly acting irreversible cholinergic drug?

    a. Neostigmine
    b. Echothiophate
    c. Pilocarpine
    d. Pralidoxime

18. When acetylcholine is released in the synaptic space, what does it do?

    a. Binds with receptors on the postsynaptic cell membrane to create an effector response.
    b. Binds to receptors on the presynaptic membrane to send a negative feedback signal.
    c. Gets degraded by acetylcholinesterase into choline and acetate.
    d. All of the above.

19. Which one of the following is NOT a muscarinic effect of acetylcholine on the heart?

    a. Decrease in heart rate
    b. Decrease in impulse conduction time
    c. Decrease in cardiac output
    d. Decrease in atrial contraction force

20. Which one of the following drugs is a directly acting cholinergic agent that is used topically – in eyedrops to treat glaucoma?

    a. Bethanechol
    b. Carbachol
    c. Edrophonium
    d. Physostigmine

21. Which one of the following drugs is an indirectly acting reversible choline agonist that is used to reverse atropine toxicity?

    a. Bethanechol
    b. Carbachol
    c. Edrophonium
    d. Physostigmine

CHAPTER 2:

Adrenergic and antiadrenergic drugs

EXERCISE 1 - ADRENERGIC AGONISTS

These are also known as adrenergic drugs or sympathomimetic drugs. They activate the adrenergic receptors either directly or indirectly by increasing the levels of norepinephrine. They are classified as:

    A.   Directly acting agonists
    B.   Indirectly acting agonists
    C.   Mixed action agonists

For each of the drugs mentioned in the table below, fill out the group to which it belongs (A or B or C).

	Drug	A or B or C
1.	Epinephrine	
2.	Amphetamines	
3.	Albuterol	
4.	Ephedrine	
5.	Terbutaline	

EXERCISE 2 - FILL IN THE BLANKS

6. Norepinephrine is synthesized from _____.

7. Tyrosine is transported from plasma into the adrenergic neuron, where the enzyme _____ converts it into DOPA (dihydroxyphenylalanine).

8. Epinephrine is a naturally occurring hormone that is formed by the _____ of norepinephrine in the adrenal medulla.

9. Epinephrine acts on both α and β receptors. At low doses, _____ effects predominate.

10. When administered as an external agent, norepinephrine influences only _____ receptors.

11. Like epinephrine, norepinephrine is rapidly metabolized by _____ and COMT.

12. Norepinephrine is indicated in the treatment of shock because it helps to increase the peripheral _____.

13. Phenylephrine is used for the treatment of _____, especially when it presents with tachycardia.

14. Clonidine is a selective _____ agonist.

15. Albuterol and terbutaline are β2 agonists used primarily via the inhalational route for managing acute _____ attacks.

EXERCISE 3 - MCQs

16. Which one of the following adrenergic receptors is responsible for producing mydriasis?

    a. α1
    b. α2
    c. β1
    d. β2

17. Which one of the following adrenergic receptors decreases cAMP production?

    a. α1
    b. α2
    c. β1
    d. β2

18. Which one of the following adrenergic receptors causes bronchodilation?

    a. α1
    b. α2
    c. β1
    d. β2

19. After its release into the synaptic cleft and interaction with postsynaptic receptors, what is the possible fate of norepinephrine?

    a. It is absorbed into the systemic circulation.
    b. It is taken back into the neuron.
    c. It is degraded in the synaptic space by catechol o-methyltransferase.
    d. All of the above.

20. Which one of the following effects of epinephrine on the cardiovascular system is NOT true?

    a. Increases myocardial contractility.
    b. Inhibits renin production.
    c. Vasoconstricts skin and visceral blood vessels.
    d. Vasodilates skeletal muscle vessels.

21. What is the benefit of combining epinephrine with local anesthetic drugs?

    a. Increased duration of action of local anesthetics.

    b. Decreased systemic toxicity of local anesthetics.

    c. Bloodless field of surgery.

    d. All of the above.

22. Dobutamine is a synthetic drug that acts exclusively on which receptors?

    a. $\alpha 1$ c. $\beta 1$

    b. $\alpha 2$ d. $\beta 2$

23. Which one of the following directly acting adrenergic agonists is used mainly topically such as in decongestant nasal sprays?

    a. Epinephrine   c. Dobutamine

    b. Dopamine   d. Oxymetazoline

24. Because of its powerful effects, which one of the following directly acting adrenergic agonists is the drug of choice in several medical emergencies, including cardiac arrest and life-threatening bronchospasm in asthma and anaphylaxis?

    a. Epinephrine   c. Dobutamine

    b. Dopamine   d. Oxymetazoline

25. The main therapeutic use of isoproterenol is in the treatment of:

    a. seizures   c. heart block

    b. nasal congestion   d. stroke

26. Which one of the following adrenergic agonists has a role in the management of withdrawal from habit-forming substances, including tobacco, opiates and benzodiazepines?

    a. Dobutamine   c. Clonidine

    b. Oxymetazoline   d. Albuterol

Peripheral Nervous System

CHAPTER 1:

Local anesthetics

EXERCISE 1 - FILL IN THE BLANKS

1. Procaine is an example of an _____-linked local anesthetic.

2. Lidocaine is an example of an _____-linked local anesthetic.

3. Local anesthetics block sensations in the following order: pain, _____, touch and deep pressure.

4. Local anesthetics do not have cardiac effects at normal doses, but at high doses, they _____ myocardial conduction and contractility.

5. The effect of local anesthetics on blood vessels is that they cause _____.

EXERCISE 2 - MCQs

6. Which one of the following is an example of an ester-linked local anesthetic?

   a. Prilocaine   c. Bupivacaine
   b. Mepivacaine   d. Tetracaine

7. The major way local anesthetics act is by blocking which channels?

   a. K   c. Cl
   b. Na   d. Ca

8. Which one of the following factors would increase the duration of action of a local anesthetic?

   a. Lower pKa
   b. Higher lipid solubility
   c. Greater protein binding
   d. Vasodilation

9. Which one of the following factors would increase the potency of a local anesthetic?

   a. Lower pKa
   b. Higher lipid solubility
   c. Greater protein binding
   d. Vasodilation

10. Which one of the following is a local anesthetic with a high potency and long duration of action?

   a. Chloroprocaine
   b. Lignocaine
   c. Prilocaine
   d. Bupivacaine

Skeletal muscle relaxants

EXERCISE 1 - FILL IN THE BLANKS

1. Neuromuscular blocking agents act at the _____ receptors of the neuromuscular junction.

2. Nondepolarizing blockers are _____ antagonists of acetylcholine.

3. The principal use of nondepolarizing blockers is during _____ to maintain a state of muscle relaxation.

4. The main depolarizing neuromuscular blocking drug in use today is _____.

EXERCISE 2 - MCQs

5. Which one of the following is an example of a short acting nondepolarizing blocker?

    a. Vecuronium   c. Mivacurium
    b. Rocuronium   d. Pancuronium

6. When an action potential in a motor neuron reaches the neuromuscular junction, which voltage-gated channels does it open on the motor axon terminal?

    a. K   c. Cl
    b. Na   d. Ca

7. Which one of the following statements is INCORRECT regarding the pharmacokinetics of nondepolarizing neuromuscular blockers?

    a. They are not effective when taken orally.
    b. They are usually administered intravenously.
    c. They can penetrate the blood brain barrier.
    d. They are mostly excreted unchanged in the urine.

8. Some patients are not able to metabolize succinylcholine. This occurs in patients who have a genetically altered form of the enzyme pseudocholinesterase. If succinylcholine is administered to such patients, they are at risk of developing:

    a. Hyperkalemia
    b. Apnea
    c. Hypertensive crisis
    d. Malignant hyperthermia

Drugs Acting on the Paracrine and Endocrine System

CHAPTER 1:

Histamine and antihistamines

EXERCISE 1 - FILL IN THE BLANKS

1. Another name for paracrine drugs is _____ drugs.

2. Endocrine compounds, or hormones, act at sites_____ from where they are produced.

3. The precursor to histamine is the amino acid _____.

4. The _____ histamine receptor is present in the presynaptic region, inhibits further histamine release and causes sedation.

EXERCISE 2 - MCQs

5. Which one of the following is a tissue that contains high amounts of histamine?

   a. Skin
   b. Gastric mucosa
   c. Lungs
   d. All of the above

6. Which one of the following cell types is responsible for the storage and release of histamine?

   a. Eosinophils
   b. T-lymphocytes
   c. Mast cells
   d. RBCs

7. The clinical actions of which one of the following types of histamine receptors are not well-known?

   a. H1   c. H3
   b. H2   d. H4

8. Which one of the following types of histamine receptors accounts for gastric acid secretion?

   a. H1   c. H3
   b. H2   d. H4

Prostaglandin inhibitors

EXERCISE 1 - FILL IN THE BLANKS

1. Prostaglandins are synthesized from _____ which is a long-chain free fatty acid that is generally present as a component of cell membranes.

2. The enzyme _____ is responsible for prostaglandin production during inflammation.

3. The enzyme lipoxygenase acts on arachidonic acid to produce _____.

4. Alprostadil is an analogue of _____.

5. _____ are a group of drugs that exert clinical effects by inhibiting the metabolic pathways that synthesize prostaglandins.

6. While most NSAIDs reversibly inhibit cyclooxygenase, _____ alters the structure of the enzyme and this action is irreversible.

7. NSAIDs are the most commonly used drugs for _____ management.

8. Low doses of aspirin are prescribed to prevent ischemic events because it hampers platelet aggregation by inhibiting _____.

EXERCISE 2 - PROSTAGLANDIN INHIBITORS: NSAIDs

Based on their mechanism of action, NSAIDS belong to the following four groups:

A. Non-selective COX inhibitors
B. Preferential COX-2 inhibitors
C. Selective COX-2 inhibitors
D. Analgesic-antipyretics with poor anti-inflammatory action

For each of the drugs mentioned in the table below, fill out the group to which it belongs (A, B, C or D).

	Drug	A, B, C or D
9.	Diclofenac	
10.	Paracetamol	
11.	Ibuprofen	
12.	Celecoxib	
13.	Aspirin	
14.	Piroxicam	

EXERCISE 3 - MCQs

15. Which one of the following prostaglandins is known to cause platelet aggregation?

a. PGI2   c. PGE2
b. TXA2   d. COX

16. Which one of the following prostaglandins is known to cause bronchodilation?

a. PGI2   c. PGE2
b. TXA2   d. COX

17. Which one of the following prostaglandins is known to have a role in the development of fever?

    a. PGI2
    b. TXA2
    c. PGE2
    d. COX

18. Which one of the following prostaglandin analogues has been used in the management of erectile dysfunction?

    a. Alprostadil
    b. Lubiprostone
    c. Misoprostol
    d. Epoprostenol

19. Which one of the following prostaglandin analogues has been used in the management of pulmonary arterial hypertension?

    a. Alprostadil
    b. Lubiprostone
    c. Misoprostol
    d. Epoprostenol

20. Which one of the following prostaglandin analogues has been used to induce labor?

    a. Alprostadil
    b. Lubiprostone
    c. Misoprostol
    d. Epoprostenol

21. Which one of the following is NOT an established therapeutic indication of NSAIDs?

    a. Anti-inflammatory
    b. Antipyretic
    c. Antiemetic
    d. Analgesic

22. Which one of the following represents the respiratory effect of NSAIDs?

    a. Raised alveolar ventilation at clinical doses
    b. Respiratory alkalosis at high doses
    c. Central respiratory paralysis at toxic doses
    d. All of the above

CHAPTER 3

Anterior pituitary drugs

EXERCISE 1 - FILL IN THE BLANKS

1. The hypothalamus secretes regulatory hormones, which are transmitted to the anterior pituitary via the _____ portal system.

2. The hypothalamus secretes _____, which acts on the anterior pituitary to secrete ACTH which is also known as corticotropin.

3. Synthetic ACTH (cosyntropin) is used to diagnose _____.

EXERCISE 2 - MCQs

4. High blood levels of which one of the following hormones would lead to a suppression in CRH and ACTH release?

    a. Calcitonin
    b. Insulin
    c. Thyroid-stimulating hormone
    d. Cortisol

5. Which one of the following hormones inhibits the secretion of growth hormone?

    a. Calcitonin
    b. Thyroid-stimulating hormone
    c. Somatotropin-releasing hormone
    d. Somatostatin

6. Which one of the following is NOT a metabolic effect associated with growth hormone?

    a. Proteolysis   c. Gluconeogenesis
    b. Lipolysis   d. Glycogenolysis

CHAPTER 4:

Thyroid hormone and inhibitors

EXERCISE 1 - FILL IN THE BLANKS

1. The two major thyroid hormones are _____ and thyroxine (T4).

2. Iodine combines with the tyrosine residue of the protein _____ to form mono-iodothyronine and di-iodothyronine.

3. Inside cells, T4 is converted into _____ which is the active form of the hormone.

EXERCISE 2 - MCQs

4. Which one of the following is NOT a metabolic effect of thyroid hormones?

    a. Glycogenolysis

    b. Gluconeogenesis

    c. Increased plasma free fatty acids

    d. Decreased basal metabolic rate

5. Which one of the following is NOT associated with increased thyroid activity?

    a. Tachycardia

    b. Increased cardiac output

    c. Weak and flabby muscles

    d. Anxiousness

6. Hypothyroidism that occurs in adults is called:

    a. Cretinism

    b. Myxedema

    c. Thyrotoxicosis

    d. Thyroid adenoma

CHAPTER 5:

Drugs used in calcium metabolism

EXERCISE 1 - FILL IN THE BLANKS

1. Usually, only about _____ of ingested calcium is absorbed.

2. One condition which needs urgent calcium replacement for its treatment is called _____.

3. Calcitonin is produced by the _____ cells of the thyroid gland.

EXERCISE 2 - MCQs

4. Which one of the following is a physiological function of calcium in the body?

    a. Required for muscle contraction
    b. Serves as an intracellular messenger
    c. Activates clotting factors
    d. All of the above

5. Which one of the following is NOT an effect of the parathyroid hormone (PTH)?

    a. Increased plasma calcium levels
    b. Decreased osteoclastic activity
    c. Increases renal calcium reabsorption
    d. Activation of the enzyme 1α hydroxylase

6. Which one of the following is used to treat osteoporosis in postmenopausal women?

    a. Insulin
    b. Parathormone
    c. Calcitonin
    d. Thyroxine

CHAPTER 6:

Insulin, glucagon and oral hypoglycemic drugs

EXERCISE 1 - FILL IN THE BLANKS

1. Insulin is a hormone that is secreted by the _____ cells of the islets of the pancreas.

2. Type 1 diabetes can only be treated by administering _____.

3. In type 2 diabetes, there is peripheral _____ to insulin.

4. Synthetic insulin cannot be given orally as it gets degraded in the GIT, it is usually administered as _____ injections.

5. Elderly patients on sulfonylureas are particularly susceptible to _____.

6. Meglitinide analogs are quick acting, so they are often used for _____ blood glucose control.

7. The only biguanide that is therapeutically used today is _____.

EXERCISE 2 - INSULIN PREPARATIONS

Depending on their onset and duration of action, insulin preparations are classified into the following four groups:

A. Rapid-acting
B. Short-acting
C. Intermediate-acting
D. Long-acting

For each of the drugs mentioned in the table below, fill out the group to which it belongs (A, B, C or D).

	Drug	A, B, C or D
8.	NPH insulin	
9.	Insulin glargine	
10.	Insulin aspart	
11.	Regular insulin	
12.	Insulin lispro	

EXERCISE 3 - MCQs

13. Type 1 diabetes is also referred to as:

    a. Diabetes insipidus
    b. Juvenile diabetes
    c. Cushing's syndrome
    d. Polydipsia

14. Which one of the following is NOT a metabolic effect of insulin?

    a. Promotes glycogenesis
    b. Inhibits gluconeogenesis
    c. Promotes triglyceride synthesis
    d. Inhibits protein synthesis

15. Which one of the following is known to occur at insulin injection sites?

    a.   Melanoma
    b.   Varicose veins
    c.   Lipodystrophy
    d.   Osteoporosis

16. Which one of the following is a second-generation sulfonylurea?

    a.   Tolbutamide
    b.   Chlorpropamide
    c.   Glyburide
    d.   Metformin

17. Which one of the following has the longest half-life?

    a.   Glyburide
    b.   Glipizide
    c.   Glimepiride
    d.   Gliclazide

18. Which one of the following is the usual initial drug of choice when commencing therapy in type 2 diabetes?

    a.   Tolbutamide
    b.   Chlorpropamide
    c.   Glyburide
    d.   Metformin

19. Which one of the following is correct regarding the pharmacokinetics of metformin?

    a.   Can be taken orally
    b.   Does not bind to plasma proteins
    c.   Is excreted unchanged in urine
    d.   All of the above

CHAPTER 7:

Corticosteroids

EXERCISE 1 – FILL IN THE BLANKS

1. The principal mineralocorticoid in the body is
   _____.

2. Cortisol exerts anti-inflammatory activity by inhibiting the enzyme
   _____.

3. The potency of other synthetic corticosteroids is measured against
   _____ as the reference.

EXERCISE 2 - MCQs

4. Which part of the adrenal gland is mainly responsible for the production of glucocorticoids?

    a. Zona glomerulosa
    b. Zona fasciculata
    c. Zona reticularis
    d. Adrenal medulla

5. Aldosterone acts at which site in the kidney to enhance sodium reabsorption?

    a. Glomerulus
    b. Proximal convoluted tubule
    c. Loop of Henle
    d. Distal convoluted tubule

6. Which one of the following is NOT a function of cortisol?

    a. Immunosuppressive effect
    b. Anti-inflammatory activity
    c. Increased urinary calcium
    d. Decreased blood glucose

CHAPTER 8:

Androgens, estrogens and progestins

EXERCISE 1 - FILL IN THE BLANKS

1. The predominant androgenic hormone is testosterone which is secreted by the _____ cells of the testes.

2. Anabolic steroids are synthetic androgens that have higher anabolic and lower _____ activity.

3. Men have a higher hematocrit relative to women because testosterone promotes _____.

4. Testosterone is usually used for the treatment of primary or secondary _____.

EXERCISE 2 - MCQs

5. Which one of the following can occur in women taking androgens?

    a. Hirsutism
    b. Deepening of voice
    c. Male pattern baldness
    d. All of the above

6. In men, excessive use of androgens can lead to which of the following?

    a. Priapism
    b. Gynecomastia
    c. Impotence
    d. All of the above

7. Finasteride, an antiandrogen, can be used to manage:

    a. Senile osteoporosis
    b. Benign prostatic hyperplasia
    c. Stunted growth
    d. Gynecomastia

8. Finasteride and dutasteride block synthesis of testosterone by inhibiting which enzyme?

    a. Phospholipase A2
    b. 1α hydroxylase
    c. Cyclooxygenase-2
    d. 5-α-reductase

Cardiovascular System

CHAPTER 1:

Drugs used in hypertension

EXERCISE 1 - FILL IN THE BLANKS

1. Most patients suffer from primary or 'essential' hypertension, where the cause is _____.

2. The initial drug group of choice for hypertension in most patients is _____.

3. The potassium-sparing diuretic spironolactone acts as an antagonist of _____.

4. The first angiotensin-converting enzyme inhibitor to find clinical use was _____.

5. The kidneys respond to low arterial pressure by releasing an enzyme called _____.

6. Angiotensin II causes vasoconstriction and also stimulates secretion of _____.

7. Since ACE inhibitors can cause _____, they should not be combined with potassium-sparing diuretics.

8. In patients with diabetes, ACE inhibitors can prevent or delay the onset of _____.

9. Due to similar effects and adverse effects, _____ should not be combined with ACE inhibitors.

10. Aliskiren is a drug that directly inhibits _____.

EXERCISE 2 - MCQs

11. Which one of the following is NOT an adverse effect caused by thiazide diuretics?

   a. Hyperglycemia   c. Hypernatremia
   b. Hyperuricemia   d. Hypokalemia

12. Which one of the following diuretics is an example of a thiazide diuretic?

   a. Acetazolamide   c. Chlorthalidone
   b. Furosemide   d. Amiloride

13. Which one of the following diuretics is best suited to manage fluid overload such as in congestive heart failure?

   a. Acetazolamide   c. Chlorthalidone
   b. Furosemide   d. Amiloride

14. Which one of the following diuretics is best suited in conditions where the development of hypokalemia is a concern?

   a. Acetazolamide   c. Chlorthalidone
   b. Furosemide   d. Amiloride

15. Which one of the following ACE inhibitors has the shortest half-life?

   a. Captopril   c. Lisinopril
   b. Enalapril   d. Ramipril

16. In which one of the following conditions, the use of ACE inhibitors has been shown to reduce mortality?

   a. Stroke
   b. Myocardial infarction
   c. Trauma
   d. Poisoning

17. Compared to ACE inhibitors, angiotensin II receptor blockers are less likely to cause urticaria and angioedema because they do not increase the levels of which one of the following?

    a. Histamine   c. Angiotensin
    b. Bradykinin   d. Renin

18. Which one of the following drugs belongs to the benzothiazepine group of calcium channel blockers?

    a. Verapamil   c. Nifedipine
    b. Diltiazem   d. Amlodipine

19. Which one of the following drugs belongs to the diphenylalkylamine group of calcium channel blockers?

    a. Verapamil   c. Nifedipine
    b. Diltiazem   d. Amlodipine

20. Which one of the following calcium channel blockers is most frequently associated with constipation?

    a. Verapamil   c. Nifedipine
    b. Diltiazem   d. Amlodipine

CHAPTER 2

Drugs for myocardial ischemia

EXERCISE 1 - FILL IN THE BLANKS

1. There are three types of angina: stable, unstable and _____ angina.

2. An example of a short-acting nitrate is _____.

3. Nitric oxide (NO) is a powerful vasodilator and acts by increasing the levels of _____ within cells.

EXERCISE 2 - MCQs

4. Which one of the following is NOT an effect of nitrates?

   a. Reduced preload
   b. Increased afterload
   c. Improved coronary flow
   d. Decreased cardiac workload

5. Which one of the following is the preferred route of administration for nitroglycerin in angina?

   a. Oral
   b. Sublingual
   c. Subcutaneous
   d. Intravenous

6. Which one of the following is a clinical indication for the use of nitrates?

   a. Angina
   b. Acute coronary syndrome
   c. Esophageal spasm
   d. All of the above

CHAPTER 3:

Drugs used in arrhythmias

EXERCISE 1 - CLASSIFICATION

Antiarrhythmic drugs have been categorized as belonging to the following classes:

- Class IA
- Class IB
- Class IC
- Class II
- Class III
- Class IV

For each of the drugs mentioned in the table below, fill out the class to which it belongs.

	Drug	Class
1.	Amiodarone	
2.	Metoprolol	
3.	Quinidine	
4.	Verapamil	
5.	Lidocaine	
6.	Flecainide	

EXERCISE 2 - FILL IN THE BLANKS

7. Class I antiarrhythmic drugs are _____ blockers.

8. Quinidine, a Class IA drug, also blocks α-adrenergic receptors and _____ receptors.

9. _____, a Class IB drug, is pharmacologically similar to lignocaine and works in a similar manner.

10. Among the three subclasses of Class I antiarrhythmic drugs, _____ is the most potent.

11. Class II antiarrhythmic drugs are _____ blockers.

EXERCISE 3 - MCQs

12. Due to its QT interval prolonging effect, quinidine can give rise to:
    a. Myocardial infarction
    b. Atrial flutter
    c. Torsades de pointes
    d. Pulseless electrical activity

13. Which one of the following is correct about disopyramide?
    a. It is a Class IB antiarrhythmic drug
    b. It has cardiac stimulant effects
    c. It has anticholinergic adverse effects
    d. It speeds up the sinus rhythm

14. Lignocaine is primarily a local anesthetic. What is its route of administration when given as an antiarrhythmic?
    a. Subcutaneous
    b. Topical
    c. Oral
    d. Intravenous

15. Which one of the following is known to be effective against resistant ventricular and supraventricular tachycardias that are not responding to other treatments?

   a. Quinidine
   b. Procainamide
   c. Lignocaine
   d. Flecainide

16. Which one of the following Class II antiarrhythmic drugs is short-acting and preferred for acute arrhythmias that require immediate management?

   a. Esmolol
   b. Metoprolol
   c. Bisoprolol
   d. Carvedilol

CHAPTER 4:

Drugs used in heart failure

EXERCISE 1 - FILL IN THE BLANKS

1. Drugs that improve the force of contraction of the heart are called _____ drugs.

2. Cardiac glycosides have their origin in the _____ plant.

3. Digoxin inhibits the enzyme _____.

EXERCISE 2 - MCQs

4. Which one of the following is NOT correct concerning the pathophysiology of heart failure?

   a. Low cardiac output decreases renal perfusion and stimulates renin release

   b. The renin-angiotensin-aldosterone system causes sodium and water retention

   c. To compensate for the reduced workload, there is hypertrophy of cardiac muscle

   d. Over time, there is decompensated heart failure and fluid retention

5. Which one of the following is an aim of therapy in heart failure?

    a. To improve inotropic effect on the heart, without increasing the workload

    b. To decrease fluid retention and promote excretion of sodium and water

    c. To inhibit the sympathetic nervous system

    d. All of the above

6. Which one of the following is NOT correct with respect to the effects of digoxin?

    a. Increases force of contraction of the heart

    b. Increases heart rate

    c. Stimulates chemoreceptor trigger zone

    d. Induces arrhythmias

Hematopoietic System

CHAPTER 1:

Hematinics and drugs affecting blood clotting

EXERCISE 1 - FILL IN THE BLANKS

1. Iron combines with storage proteins such as ferritin or transport proteins such as _____.

2. Iron is absorbed from the intestine mainly in the_____ form.

3. Oral iron supplementation can give rise to _____ stools.

4. Folate deficiency characteristically leads to _____ anemia.

5. In pernicious anemia, gastric parietal cells fail to produce the 'intrinsic factor' required for the absorption of _____.

EXERCISE 2 - MCQs

6. Which one of the following is an example of a parenteral preparation of iron?

   a. Iron dextran
   b. Ferrous sulphate
   c. Ferrous gluconate
   d. Ferrous aluminum citrate

7. A patient with rheumatoid arthritis is being treated by methotrexate. Supplementation with which one of the following would be necessary?

   a. Iron
   b. Calcium
   c. Folic acid
   d. Glucose

8. Which one of the following sites of the intestine accounts for the most folate absorption?

   a. Jejunum
   b. Ileum
   c. Ascending colon
   d. Sigmoid colon

9. Which one of the following is correct about erythropoietin?

   a. It is synthesized naturally in the kidney
   b. It stimulates the production of red blood cells
   c. Its supplementation is required in end-stage renal disease
   d. All of the above

10. Hydroxyurea is indicated in which one of the following types of anemia?

    a. Sickle cell anemia
    b. Pernicious anemia
    c. Megaloblastic anemia
    d. Iron-deficiency anemia

Respiratory System

Drugs used in cough and bronchial asthma

EXERCISE 1 - FILL IN THE BLANKS

1. Opioids act as antitussives by elevating the stimulus threshold in the _____.

2. Opioids must not be used in patients with asthma as they can cause _____.

3. Dextromethorphan is a synthetic _____ receptor antagonist.

4. _____ is a plant product which enhances mucociliary function and decreases the viscosity of secretions.

EXERCISE 2 - MCQs

5. Which one of the following antitussives acts peripherally to suppress the cough reflex receptors that are located in the lungs and respiratory passages?

   a. Codeine
   b. Benzonatate
   c. Dextromethorphan
   d. Ethylmorphine

6. Which one of the following patients should NOT be prescribed an antitussive?

   a. A patient with cough who has had recent eye surgery
   b. A patient with cough who has had recent hernia surgery
   c. A patient with cough that produces a lot of mucus
   d. A patient with dry cough that doesn't let him sleep

7. Which one of the following expectorants acts as a mucolytic by breaking down the disulphide bonds in mucus proteins?

   a. Guaifenesin
   b. Bromhexine
   c. Ambroxol
   d. Acetylcysteine

8. Following are some examples of β-2 agonists used in patients with asthma. Which one of them is long-acting?

   a. Albuterol
   b. Levalbuterol
   c. Salmeterol
   d. Terbutaline

Gastrointestinal System

Drugs used for diseases of the GI tract

EXERCISE 1 - FILL IN THE BLANKS

1. Ranitidine blocks _____ receptors in the stomach and decreases gastric acid production.

2. Antacids are substances that have a _____ pH.

3. Antacids are mostly used to provide immediate symptomatic relief as prolonged use can lead to a compensatory _____.

4. Chemically, milk of magnesia contains _____.

5. Sucralfate is an aluminum salt of _____.

EXERCISE 2 - MCQs

6. Which one of the following inhibits gastric acid secretion?

   a. Histamine
   c. Gastrin
   b. Acetylcholine
   d. Prostaglandins

7. Which one of the following drugs is an example of a proton pump inhibitor?

   a. Famotidine
   c. Nizatidine
   b. Lansoprazole
   d. Misoprostol

8. It is generally advised to NOT take clopidogrel with which one of the following group of drugs?

   a. Antacids
   b. H2 antagonists
   c. Proton pump inhibitors
   d. Prostaglandin analogues

9. Which one of the following is NOT correct about misoprostol?

   a. It is a synthetic analogue of PGE1
   b. It stimulates gastric mucous and bicarbonate secretion
   c. It is indicated as prophylaxis for ulcers in patients taking NSAIDS
   d. It is safe to use in pregnant patients

10. Which one of the following drugs acts by forming a gel that acts as a physical barrier between the gastric mucosa and acidic secretion?

    a. Ranitidine
    b. Sucralfate
    c. Misoprostol
    d. Milk of magnesia

UNIT X

Genitourinary System

Diuretics

EXERCISE 1 - FILL IN THE BLANKS

1. Paradoxically, _____ diuretics have been used to treat diabetes insipidus.

2. The continued antihypertensive effect of thiazide diuretics is because they decrease the _____ resistance.

3. The diuretic _____ is well-known to cause gynecomastia.

4. A patient on amiloride should be closely monitored for _____.

5. Eplerenone is an antagonist of the _____ receptor.

EXERCISE 2 - MCQs

6. Which one of the following groups of diuretic drugs is considered high-ceiling?

    a. Thiazide diuretics
    b. Potassium-sparing diuretics
    c. Loop diuretics
    d. Osmotic diuretics

7. Which one of the following groups of diuretic drugs is considered medium-efficacy?

    a. Thiazide diuretics
    b. Potassium-sparing diuretics
    c. Loop diuretics
    d. Osmotic diuretics

8. Which one of the following types of edema can be treated with furosemide?

    a. Edema of hepatic, renal or cardiac origin
    b. Acute pulmonary edema
    c. Cerebral edema
    d. All of the above

9. Which one of the following groups of diuretics has been associated with ototoxicity?

    a. Thiazide diuretics
    b. Potassium-sparing diuretics
    c. Loop diuretics
    d. Osmotic diuretics

10. Potassium-sparing diuretics primarily act on which site of the nephron?

    a. Glomerulus
    b. Proximal convoluted tubule
    c. Loop of Henle
    d. Collecting tubule

11. Which diuretic has a known role in the prevention and treatment of acute mountain sickness?

    a. Acetazolamide
    b. Furosemide
    c. Amiloride
    d. Chlorthalidone

EXERCISE 3 - LABEL THE PICTURE

Label the five categories of diuretics in terms of their mechanism of action in the image below.

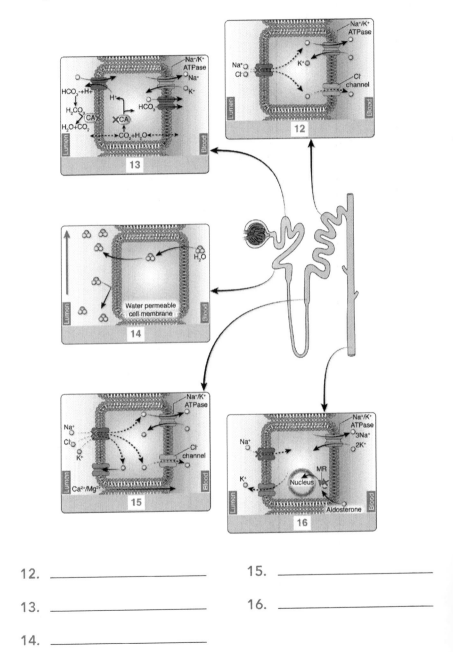

12. _____   15. _____

13. _____   16. _____

14. _____

UNIT XI

Antimicrobial Drugs

CHAPTER 1:

Antibacterials

EXERCISE 1 - FILL IN THE BLANKS

1. Drugs used in antimicrobial therapy have the capacity to kill microorganisms without damaging _____ cells.

2. Antibiotics are selected _____ or after sensitivity testing.

3. Beta-lactam antibiotics act by inhibiting _____ synthesis.

4. Penicillin V is administered by the _____ route.

5. Orally taken penicillins can disturb intestinal _____.

6. Carbapenems are synthetic _____ antibiotics.

7. Clavulanic acid is an inhibitor of _____.

8. Tetracyclines bind to the _____ subunit of the bacterial ribosome and prevent protein synthesis.

EXERCISE 2 - MCQs

9. Which one of the following penicillins is resistant to penicillinase?

   a. Penicillin G
   b. Penicillin V
   c. Methicillin
   d. Amoxicillin

10. Which one of the following adverse events has been linked to penicillin use?

   a. Hypersensitivity reactions
   b. Diarrhea
   c. Neurotoxicity
   d. All of the above

11. Which one of the following cephalosporins is third generation?

   a. Cefepime
   b. Ceftriaxone
   c. Cefuroxime
   d. Cefazolin

12. Carbapenems as a class of antibiotics are generally administered:

   a. Orally
   b. Intrathecally
   c. Parenterally
   d. Topically

13. Imipenem is administered in combination with which one of the following?

   a. Clavulanic acid
   b. Glucose
   c. Cilastatin
   d. Epinephrine

14. Which one of the following is an example of a monobactam?

   a. Piperacillin
   b. Aztreonam
   c. Meropenem
   d. Cefixime

15. Which one of the following is correct about vancomycin?

   a. Effective against methicillin-resistant Staphylococcus aureus
   b. Effective against Clostridium difficile
   c. Causes dose-related ototoxicity and nephrotoxicity
   d. All of the above

16. The use of tetracyclines in young growing children is associated with:

   a. Teratogenicity
   b. Teeth discoloration
   c. Growth spurt
   d. Low cost of treatment

CHAPTER 2:

Antivirals

EXERCISE 1 - FILL IN THE BLANKS

1. Viruses are _____ parasites which use the host cell's metabolic machinery to survive.

2. Amantadine has been used against the _____ virus.

3. The preferred route of administration for zanamivir is _____.

4. Interferon _____ is available for clinical use in the treatment of viral hepatitis.

5. Adefovir has an established role in the treatment of _____ virus infection.

6. _____, a drug used in viral hepatitis, acts by competing with deoxyguanosine triphosphate.

EXERCISE 2 - MCQs

7. Which one of the following antiviral drugs is an example of a viral neuraminidase inhibitor?

    a. Entecavir
    b. Rimantadine
    c. Adefovir
    c. Zanamivir

8. Which one of the following antiviral drugs is an example of a viral M2 protein inhibitor?

    a. Entecavir
    b. Rimantadine
    c. Adefovir
    d. Zanamivir

9. Which one of the following antiviral drugs is effective against both influenza A and B viruses?

    a. Entecavir
    b. Rimantadine
    c. Adefovir
    d. Zanamivir

10. Which one of the following is a protease inhibitor used in the treatment of hepatitis C?

    a. Boceprevir
    b. Telbivudine
    c. Entecavir
    d. Adefovir

11. Which one of the following is the drug of choice for treatment of cytomegalovirus infections?

    a. Telbivudine
    b. Ganciclovir
    c. Cidofovir
    d. Acyclovir

12. Which one of the following is the drug of choice for treatment of herpes infections?

    a. Telbivudine
    b. Ganciclovir
    c. Cidofovir
    d. Acyclovir

CHAPTER 3

Antifungal drugs

EXERCISE 1 - FILL IN THE BLANKS

1. The medical term for an infection or disease caused by a fungus is
   _____.

2. Amphotericin B binds to a compound called _____ in
   fungal cell membranes.

3. Amphotericin B has a _____ therapeutic index.

EXERCISE 2 - MCQs

4.   Which one of the following is correct about flucytosine (5-FC)?

   a.   It is a purine analog
   b.   It is less effective when give with amphotericin B
   c.   It is well absorbed when given orally
   d.   It cannot reach the CSF

5.   Which one of the following antifungal drugs acts by inhibiting the conversion of lanosterol to ergosterol?

   a.   Flucytosine
   b.   Amphotericin B
   c.   Caspofungin
   d.   Fluconazole

6.   Which one of the following antifungal drugs acts by inhibiting the synthesis of β-D-glucan in the fungal cell wall?

   a.   Flucytosine
   b.   Amphotericin B
   c.   Caspofungin
   d.   Fluconazole

CHAPTER 4:

Antiprotozoal and anthelmintic drugs

EXERCISE 1 - FILL IN THE BLANKS

1. Asymptomatic amebiasis can be treated with a _____ amebicide.

2. A well-known side effect of metronidazole is that it can leave a _____ taste in your mouth.

3. In cases of metronidazole intolerance, _____ can be used as it has a similar mechanism of action and indications.

4. Dehydroemetine is administered as an _____ injection.

5. Malaria is a protozoal infection that is transmitted to humans through the female _____ mosquito.

EXERCISE 2 - MCQs

6. A patient presents with diarrhea that has developed after antibiotic use. A stool test reveals C. difficile toxins. Which one of the following is an effective drug treatment?

   a. Amoxicillin
   b. Iodoquinol

   c. Dehydroemetine
   d. Metronidazole

7. Which one of the following is a clinical use indication for metronidazole?

   a. Amebiasis
   b. Giardiasis

   c. H. pylori infection
   d. All of the above

8. Which one of the following is considered a 'luminal amebicide'?

   a. Amoxicillin
   b. Iodoquinol

   c. Dehydroemetine
   d. Metronidazole

9. Which one of the following antimalarial drugs is effective only against the exo-erythrocytic forms of malaria?

   a. Chloroquine
   b. Artemisinin

   c. Pyrimethamine
   d. Primaquine

10. Which one of the following antimalarial drugs acts by preventing conversion of heme to hemozoin?

   a. Chloroquine
   b. Artemisinin

   c. Pyrimethamine
   d. Primaquine

Important Miscellaneous Drugs

CHAPTER 1:

Anticancer drugs and immunosuppressants

EXERCISE 1 - FILL IN THE BLANKS

1. _____ are a class of anticancer drugs that have chemical structures similar to normal cellular compounds, so they interfere with normal cellular metabolism.

2. _____, an antitumor antibiotic, is a metal ion chelating agent which cleaves DNA through oxidative processes.

3. Cyclophosphamide ultimately breaks down into two cytotoxic metabolites: _____ mustard and acrolein.

4. Carmustine is given intravenously, while lomustine is given _____.

5. Nitrosoureas are predominantly used in the management of _____ tumors.

EXERCISE 2 - MCQs

6. Which one of the following drugs is an analog of folic acid?

   a. 6-Mercaptopurine
   b. Methotrexate

   c. Cytarabine
   d. 5-Fluorouracil

7. Which one of the following drugs is an analog of 2-deoxycytidine?

   a. 6-Mercaptopurine
   b. Methotrexate

   c. Cytarabine
   d. 5-Fluorouracil

8. Which one of the following drugs has found use in the management of acute lymphocytic leukemia as well as Crohn's disease?

   a. 6-Mercaptopurine
   b. Methotrexate

   c. Cytarabine
   d. 5-Fluorouracil

9. Which one of the following is correct about anthracyclines?

   a. They include the drugs doxorubicin, daunorubicin and idarubicin
   b. They release free radicals, which can damage DNA and cause membrane lipid peroxidation
   c. Their major drawback is cardiotoxicity
   d. All of the above

10. Which one of the following drugs is a nitrosourea?

   a. Doxorubicin
   b. Ifosfamide

   c. Lomustine
   d. Bleomycin

Answers

UNIT I
The Basics

Chapter 1: Routes of drug administration

EXERCISE 1 - FILL IN THE BLANKS

1. properties
2. systemic
3. nasal
4. intrathecal
5. skin
6. oral
7. blood/vascular/capillary supply
8. first-pass metabolism

EXERCISE 2 - MCQs

9. d	13. d
10. b	14. a
11. c	15. b
12. c	

Chapter 2: Drug-body interactions: pharmacokinetics and pharmacodynamics

EXERCISE 1 - FILL IN THE BLANKS

1. Pharmacokinetics
2. Pharm=acodynamics
3. bioavailability
4. cell membrane
5. low
6. microvilli
7. blood-brain barrier

EXERCISE 2 - MCQs

8. b	11. d
9. b	12. a
10. a	

EXERCISE 3 - LABEL THE PICTURE

13. Transmembrane ligand-gated ion channels
14. Transmembrane G-protein-coupled receptors
15. Enzyme-linked receptors
16. Intracellular receptors

UNIT II
Central Nervous System

Chapter 1: General anesthetics

EXERCISE 1 - FILL IN THE BLANKS

1. consciousness
2. before/prior to
3. Antiemetic

4. inhalational
5. induction
6. skeletal muscle relaxants
7. low
8. anesthetic gas/inhalational anesthetic

EXERCISE 2 - MCQs

9. d   14. d
10. d   15. c
11. b   16. b
12. d   17. b
13. b

Chapter 2: Sedative-hypnotic drugs

EXERCISE 1 - FILL IN THE BLANKS

1. hypnotics
2. GABA
3. fetal
4. psychological
5. stress

EXERCISE 2 - MCQs

6. c
7. b
8. d
9. a
10. a

Chapter 3: Opioid analgesics

EXERCISE 1 - FILL IN THE BLANKS

1. endorphins
2. δ/delta
3. morphine
4. Oxycodone
5. first-pass metabolism

EXERCISE 2 - MCQs

6. d
7. b
8. c

Chapter 4: Antidepressants and anti-anxiety drugs

EXERCISE 1 - FILL IN THE BLANKS

1. mania
2. neurotransmitters
3. reuptake
4. norepinephrine
5. chronic pain
6. Duloxetine

EXERCISE 2 - MCQs

7. a   10. c
8. d   11. c
9. b   12. b

Chapter 5: Antipsychotic drugs

EXERCISE 1 - FILL IN THE BLANKS

1. schizophrenia
2. mesolimbic
3. neurolept

EXERCISE 2 - MCQs

4. a
5. c
6. b

Chapter 6: Drugs used in Parkinsonism

EXERCISE 1 - FILL IN THE BLANKS

1. muscle movements
2. acetylcholine
3. postural hypotension

EXERCISE 2 - MCQs

4. b
5. c
6. a

Chapter 7: Anti-epileptic drugs

EXERCISE 1 - FILL IN THE BLANKS

7. Absence
8. Status epilepticus
9. Atonic

EXERCISE 2 - MCQs

10. c
11. b
12. c

UNIT III
Autonomic Nervous System

Chapter 1: Cholinergic and anticholinergic drugs

EXERCISE 1 - SYMPATHETIC OR PARASYMPATHETIC

1. P	4. S
2. P	5. P
3. P	

EXERCISE 2 - FILL IN THE BLANKS

6. autonomic ganglia
7. adrenergic
8. muscarinic
9. choline acetyltransferase
10. M3
11. Neostigmine
12. myasthenia gravis
13. Alzheimer's disease

EXERCISE 3 - MCQs

14. c	18. d
15. b	19. b
16. c	20. b
17. b	21. d

Chapter 2: Adrenergic and antiadrenergic drugs

EXERCISE 1 - ADRENERGIC AGONISTS

1. A	4. C
2. B	5. A
3. A	

EXERCISE 2 - FILL IN THE BLANKS

6. dopamine
7. tyrosine hydroxylase
8. methylation
9. β
10. α
11. MAO/monoamine oxidase
12. vascular resistance
13. hypotension
14. α2
15. asthma

EXERCISE 3 - MCQs

16. a	22. c
17. b	23. d
18. d	24. a
19. d	25. c
20. b	26. c
21. d	

UNIT IV
Peripheral Nervous System

Chapter 1: Local anesthetics

EXERCISE 1 - FILL IN THE BLANKS

1. ester
2. amide
3. temperature
4. decrease
5. vasodilation

EXERCISE 2 - MCQs

6. d	9. b
7. b	10. d
8. c	

Chapter 2: Skeletal muscle relaxants

EXERCISE 1 - FILL IN THE BLANKS

1. nicotinic
2. competitive
3. general anesthesia
4. succinylcholine

EXERCISE 2 - MCQs

5. c	7. c
6. d	8. b

UNIT V
Drugs Acting on the Paracrine and Endocrine System

Chapter 1: Histamine and antihistamines

EXERCISE 1 - FILL IN THE BLANKS

1. autacoid
2. distant/away
3. histidine
4. H3

EXERCISE 2 - MCQs

5. d	7. d
6. c	8. b

Chapter 2: Prostaglandin inhibitors

EXERCISE 1 - FILL IN THE BLANKS

1. arachidonic acid
2. COX-2

3. leukotrienes
4. PGE1
5. NSAIDs
6. aspirin
7. pain
8. thromboxane/TXA2

EXERCISE 2 - PROSTAGLANDIN INHIBITORS: NSAIDs

9. B	12. C
10. D	13. A
11. A	14. A

EXERCISE 3 - MCQs

15. b	19. d
16. c	20. c
17. c	21. c
18. a	22. d

Chapter 3: Anterior pituitary drugs

EXERCISE 1 - FILL IN THE BLANKS

1. hypothalamo-hypophyseal
2. corticotropin releasing hormone (CRH)
3. adrenal insufficiency

EXERCISE 2 - MCQs

4. d
5. d
6. a

Chapter 4: Thyroid hormone and inhibitors

EXERCISE 1 - FILL IN THE BLANKS

1. tri-iodothyronine (T3)
2. thyroglobulin
3. T3

EXERCISE 2 - MCQs

4. d
5. c
6. b

Chapter 5: Drugs used in calcium metabolism

EXERCISE 1 - FILL IN THE BLANKS

1. one-third
2. tetany
3. parafollicular (C cells)

EXERCISE 2 - MCQs

4. d
5. b
6. c

Chapter 6: Insulin, glucagon and oral hypoglycemic drugs

EXERCISE 1 - FILL IN THE BLANKS

1. beta
2. insulin
3. resistance
4. subcutaneous
5. hypoglycemia
6. postprandial
7. metformin

EXERCISE 2 - INSULIN PREPARATIONS

8. C
9. D
10. A
11. B
12. A

EXERCISE 3 - MCQs

13. b
14. d
15. c
16. c
17. d
18. d
19. d

Chapter 7: Corticosteroids

EXERCISE 1 - FILL IN THE BLANKS

1. aldosterone
2. phospholipase A2
3. hydrocortisone

EXERCISE 2 - MCQs

4. b
5. d
6. d

Chapter 8: Androgens, estrogens and progestins

EXERCISE 1 - FILL IN THE BLANKS

1. Leydig
2. androgenic
3. erythropoiesis
4. hypogonadism

EXERCISE 2 - MCQs

5. d
6. d
7. b
8. d

UNIT VI
Cardiovascular System

Chapter 1: Drugs used in hypertension

EXERCISE 1 - FILL IN THE BLANKS

1. not known/unknown
2. diuretics
3. aldosterone
4. captopril
5. renin
6. aldosterone
7. hyperkalemia
8. end stage renal disease
9. angiotensin II receptor blockers
10. renin

EXERCISE 2 - MCQs

11.	c	16.	b
12.	c	17.	b
13.	b	18.	b
14.	d	19.	a
15.	a	20.	a

Chapter 2: Drugs for myocardial ischemia

EXERCISE 1 - FILL IN THE BLANKS

1. variant (or Prinzmetal)
2. glyceryl trinitrate or nitroglycerin
3. cyclic GMP

EXERCISE 2 - MCQs

4. b
5. b
6. d

Chapter 3: Drugs used in arrhythmias

EXERCISE 1 - CLASSIFICATION

1.	III	4.	IV
2.	II	5.	IB
3.	IA	6.	IC

EXERCISE 2 - FILL IN THE BLANKS

7. sodium channel
8. cholinergic
9. Mexiletine
10. Class IC
11. beta

EXERCISE 3 - MCQs

12.	c	15.	d
13.	c	16.	a
14.	d		

Chapter 4: Drugs used in heart failure

EXERCISE 1 - FILL IN THE BLANKS

1. inotropic
2. foxglove
3. Na+/K+ ATPase

EXERCISE 2 - MCQs

4. c
5. d
6. b

UNIT VII
Hematopoietic System

Chapter 1: Hematinics and drugs affecting blood clotting

EXERCISE 1 - FILL IN THE BLANKS

1. transferrin
2. ferrous
3. black/dark
4. megaloblastic
5. vitamin B12

EXERCISE 2 - MCQs

6.	a	9.	d
7.	c	10.	a
8.	a		

UNIT VIII
Respiratory System

Chapter 1: Drugs used in cough and bronchial asthma

EXERCISE 1 - FILL IN THE BLANKS

1. central cough center
2. respiratory depression
3. NMDA
4. Guaifenesin

EXERCISE 2 - MCQs

5. b	7. d
6. c	8. c

UNIT IX
Gastrointestinal System

Chapter 1: Drugs used for diseases of the GI tract

EXERCISE 1 - FILL IN THE BLANKS

1. histamine type 2
2. high
3. acid rebound
4. magnesium hydroxide
5. sucrose

EXERCISE 2 - MCQs

6. d	9. d
7. b	10. b
8. c	

UNIT X
Genitourinary System

Chapter 1: Diuretics

EXERCISE 1 - FILL IN THE BLANKS

1. thiazide
2. peripheral vascular
3. spironolactone
4. hyperkalemia
5. aldosterone

EXERCISE 2 - MCQs

6. c	9. c
7. a	10. d
8. d	11. a

EXERCISE 3 - LABEL THE PICTURE

12. Thiazide diuretics
13. Carbonic anhydrase inhibitors
14. Osmotic diuretics
15. Loop diuretics
16. Potassium-sparing diuretics

UNIT XI
Antimicrobial Drugs

Chapter 1: Antibacterials

EXERCISE 1 - FILL IN THE BLANKS

1. host
2. empirically
3. cell wall
4. oral
5. flora
6. beta-lactam
7. beta-lactamase
8. 30S

EXERCISE 2 - MCQs

9. c	13. c
10. d	14. b
11. b	15. d
12. c	16. b

Chapter 2: Antivirals

EXERCISE 1 - FILL IN THE BLANKS

1. intracellular
2. influenza A
3. inhalation/oral inhalation
4. α
5. hepatitis B
6. Entecavir

EXERCISE 2 - MCQs

7. d	10. a
8. b	11. b
9. d	12. d

Chapter 3: Antifungal drugs

EXERCISE 1 - FILL IN THE BLANKS

1. mycosis
2. ergosterol
3. low/narrow

EXERCISE 2 - MCQs

4. c
5. d
6. c

Chapter 4: Antiprotozoal and anthelmintic drugs

EXERCISE 1 - FILL IN THE BLANKS

1. luminal
2. metallic
3. tinidazole
4. intramuscular
5. Anopheles

EXERCISE 2 - MCQs

6. d
7. d
8. b
9. d
10. a

UNIT XII
Important Miscellaneous Drugs

Chapter 1: Anticancer drugs and immunosuppressants

EXERCISE 1 - FILL IN THE BLANKS

1. Antimetabolites
2. Bleomycin
3. phosphoramide
4. orally
5. brain

EXERCISE 2 - MCQs

6. b
7. c
8. a
9. d
10. c

CHECK OUT OUR OTHER BOOKS

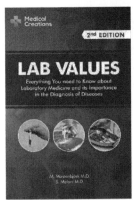
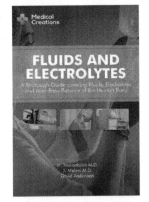
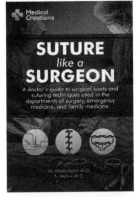

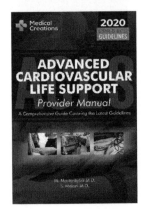

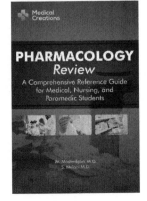

amazon.com/medicalcreations

Made in the USA
Monee, IL
31 May 2023

35037916R00066